MAKING THE GRADE

EASY POPULAR PIECES FOR YOUNG CLARINETTISTS. SELECTED AND ARRAN(

	PIANO SCORE	CLARINET PART
Any Dream Will Do	3	3
The Skater's Waltz	4	3
Eensy, Weensy Spider	5	4
Pavane (Warlock)	6	4
I'm Popeye The Sailor Man	7	5
Edelweiss	8	5
O No, John!	10	6
Sarabande (Handel)	11	6
I Have A Dream	12	7
The Yellow Rose Of Texas	14	8
Jean de Florette (Theme)	15	8
No Matter What	16	9
Hey Hey Are You Ready To Play (Tweenies Theme)	18	10
Guantanamera	20	10
Barbie Girl	22	11
The Phantom Of The Opera	23	12
Land Of Hope And Glory	24	12
All My Loving	26	13
Somethin' Stupid	28	14
Oom Pah Pah	30	14
Dance To Your Daddy	32	15

Published by
Chester Music
8/9 Frith Street, London W1D 3JB, England.

Exclusive Distributors:
Music Sales Limited
Distribution Centre, Newmarket Road, Bury St. Edmunds, Suffolk IP33 3YB, England.
Music Sales Pty Limited
120 Rothschild Avenue, Rosebery, NSW 2018, Australia.

Music arranged and processed by Jerry Lanning.
Edited by Heather Ramage.
Printed in the United Kingdom by Caligraving Limited, Thetford, Norfolk.

CD recorded, mixed and mastered by Jonas Persson.
Clarinet by John Whelan

www.musicsales.com

Chester Music
part of The Music Sales Group
London/New York/Paris/Sydney/Copenhagen/Berlin/Madrid/Tokyo

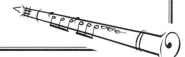

INTRODUCTION

This collection of 21 popular tunes has been carefully arranged and graded to provide attractive teaching repertoire for young clarinettists. The familiarity of the material will stimulate pupils' enthusiasm and encourage their practice.

The technical demands of the solo part increase progressively up to the standard of Associated Board Grade 1. The piano accompaniments are simple yet effective and should be within the range of most pianists.

Breath marks are given throughout, showing the most musically desirable places to take a breath.

ANY DREAM WILL DO

(from "Joseph and the Amazing Technicolor® Dreamcoat")

Music by Andrew Lloyd Webber. Lyrics by Tim Rice

Take care with the dotted rhythms. Keep the semiquavers light and try to match the accompaniment.

THE SKATER'S WALTZ

By Emil Waldteufel

Try to play the last eight bars in a single breath.

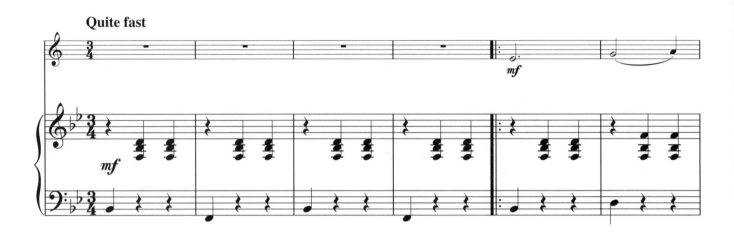

EENSY, WEENSY SPIDER

American traditional

You'll need to snatch a quick breath in bar 16. Don't be late on the second beat!

Quite lively

PAVANE

(from "The Capriol Suite")

By Peter Warlock

Try for a smooth, sustained sound, but be sure to tongue each note quite firmly.

Very steady

I'M POPEYE THE SAILOR MAN

Words & Music by Sammy Lerner

This piece needs a bright and breezy performance!

EDELWEISS

(from "The Sound of Music")

Words by Oscar Hammerstein II. Music by Richard Rodgers

Play each phrase as smoothly as possible. Listen carefully to the tuning.

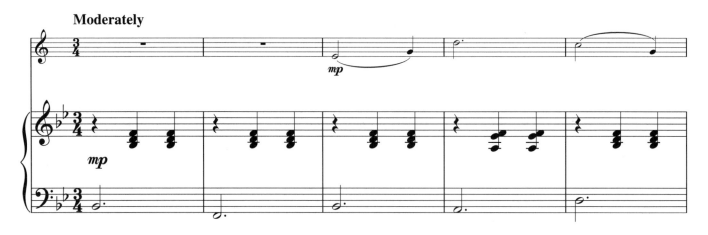

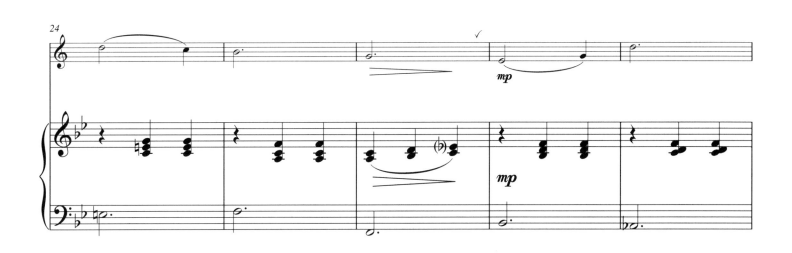

O NO, JOHN!

English traditional

Play the last four bars quite forcefully, for contrast.

S A R A B A N D E

(from "Keyboard Suite IX")

By George Frideric Handel

In this piece it's probably best to breathe every two bars.

Very slow and stately

I HAVE A DREAM

Words & Music by Benny Andersson & Björn Ulvaeus

Make sure you always take a full breath, even though most of the phrases are short.

THE YELLOW ROSE OF TEXAS

American traditional

Play with a full sound, and make sure you tongue each note.

JEAN DE FLORETTE (THEME)

By Jean-Claude Petit

Take your breaths quickly, so that you don't have to cut the dotted minims too short.

NO MATTER WHAT

Music by Andrew Lloyd Webber. Words by Jim Steinman

Take care with the start of each phrase. It's very easy to be late!

MAKING THE GRADE · GRADE 1

EASY POPULAR PIECES FOR YOUNG CLARINETTISTS. SELECTED AND ARRANGED BY JERRY LANNING

CLARINET PART

Any Dream Will Do	3
The Skater's Waltz	3
Eensy, Weensy Spider	4
Pavane (Warlock)	4
I'm Popeye The Sailor Man	5
Edelweiss	5
O No, John!	6
Sarabande (Handel)	6
I Have A Dream	7
The Yellow Rose Of Texas	8
Jean de Florette (Theme)	8
No Matter What	9
Hey Hey Are You Ready To Play (Tweenies Theme)	10
Guantanamera	10
Barbie Girl	11
The Phantom Of The Opera	12
Land Of Hope And Glory	12
All My Loving	13
Somethin' Stupid	14
Oom Pah Pah	14
Dance To Your Daddy	15

Chester Music
part of The Music Sales Group
London/New York/Paris/Sydney/Copenhagen/Berlin/Madrid/Tokyo

Published by
Chester Music
8/9 Frith Street, London W1D 3JB, England.

Exclusive Distributors:
Music Sales Limited
Distribution Centre, Newmarket Road, Bury St. Edmunds, Suffolk IP33 3YB, England.
Music Sales Pty Limited
120 Rothschild Avenue, Rosebery, NSW 2018, Australia.

Order No. CH67353-01
This book © Copyright 2003 by Chester Music.

Music arranged and processed by Jerry Lanning.
Edited by Heather Ramage.
Printed in the United Kingdom by Caligraving Limited, Thetford, Norfolk.

www.musicsales.com

ANY DREAM WILL DO

(from "Joseph and the Amazing Technicolor® Dreamcoat")

Music by Andrew Lloyd Webber. Lyrics by Tim Rice

Take care with the dotted rhythms. Keep the semiquavers light and try to match the accompaniment.

Moderately

THE SKATER'S WALTZ

By Emil Waldteufel

Try to play the last eight bars in a single breath.

Quite fast

3

EENSY, WEENSY SPIDER

American traditional

You'll need to snatch a quick breath in bar 16. Don't be late on the second beat!

Quite lively

PAVANE

(from "The Capriol Suite")

By Peter Warlock

Try for a smooth, sustained sound, but be sure to tongue each note quite firmly.

Very steady

I'M POPEYE THE SAILOR MAN

Words & Music by Sammy Lerner

This piece needs a bright and breezy performance!

EDELWEISS

(from "The Sound of Music")

Words by Oscar Hammerstein II. Music by Richard Rodgers

Play each phrase as smoothly as possible. Listen carefully to the tuning.

O NO, JOHN!

English traditional

Play the last four bars quite forcefully, for contrast.

SARABANDE

(from "Keyboard Suite IX")

By George Frideric Handel

In this piece it's probably best to breathe every two bars.

I HAVE A DREAM

Words & Music by Benny Andersson & Björn Ulvaeus

Make sure you always take a full breath, even though most of the phrases are short.

Moderately

7

THE YELLOW ROSE OF TEXAS

American traditional

Play with a full sound, and make sure you tongue each note.

JEAN DE FLORETTE (THEME)

By Jean-Claude Petit

Take your breaths quickly, so that you don't have to cut the dotted minims too short.

NO MATTER WHAT

Music by Andrew Lloyd Webber. Words by Jim Steinman

Take care with the start of each phrase. It's very easy to be late!

HEY HEY ARE YOU READY TO PLAY

(Tweenies Theme)

Music by Graham Pike & Liz Kitchen. Words by Will Brenton & Ian Lauchlan

Listen hard to the tuning of the octave leaps. Keep the rhythm relaxed.

GUANTANAMERA

Music adaptation by Pete Seeger & Julian Orbon. Words adapted by Julian Orbon from a poem by José Marti

Keep the rhythm very steady. When a phrase ends with a quaver, play the quaver lightly.

BARBIE GIRL

Words & Music by Soren Rasted, Claus Norreen, Rene Dif,
Lene Nystrom, Johnny Pederson & Karsten Delgado

Take a good breath on the first beat of bar 6, to carry you through to the end of the phrase.

THE PHANTOM OF THE OPERA

(from "The Phantom of the Opera")

Music by Andrew Lloyd Webber. Lyrics by Charles Hart. Additional Lyrics by Richard Stilgoe & Mike Batt.

Be absolutely precise with the dotted crotchet/quaver rhythms.

LAND OF HOPE AND GLORY

By Edward Elgar

Try for a very smooth, sustained sound. Don't let the tempo drag.

ALL MY LOVING

Words & Music by John Lennon & Paul McCartney

Be careful to read the rhythms carefully – don't guess!

SOMETHIN' STUPID

Words & Music by C. Carson Parks

Articulate the repeated quavers neatly and evenly.

OOM PAH PAH

(from "Oliver")

Words & Music by Lionel Bart

This piece needs a strong performance, but the middle section should be softer and smoother for contrast.

14

DANCE TO YOUR DADDY

English traditional

Accent the first beat of each bar slightly, but play the other notes quite lightly.

poco rit.

HEY HEY ARE YOU READY TO PLAY

(Tweenies Theme)

Music by Graham Pike & Liz Kitchen. Words by Will Brenton & Ian Lauchlan

Listen hard to the tuning of the octave leaps. Keep the rhythm relaxed.

GUANTANAMERA

Music adaptation by Pete Seeger & Julian Orbon. Words adapted by Julian Orbon from a poem by José Marti

Keep the rhythm very steady. When a phrase ends with a quaver, play the quaver lightly.

BARBIE GIRL

Words & Music by Soren Rasted, Claus Norreen, Rene Dif,
Lene Nystrom, Johnny Pederson & Karsten Delgado

Take a good breath on the first beat of bar 6, to carry you through to the end of the phrase.

THE PHANTOM OF THE OPERA

(from "The Phantom of the Opera")

Music by Andrew Lloyd Webber. Lyrics by Charles Hart. Additional Lyrics by Richard Stilgoe & Mike Batt.

Be absolutely precise with the dotted crotchet/quaver rhythms.

LAND OF HOPE AND GLORY

By Edward Elgar

Try for a very smooth, sustained sound. Don't let the tempo drag.

ALL MY LOVING

Words & Music by John Lennon & Paul McCartney

Be careful to read the rhythms carefully – don't guess!

SOMETHIN' STUPID

Words & Music by C. Carson Parks

Articulate the repeated quavers neatly and evenly.

Moderately

OOM PAH PAH

(from "Oliver")

Words & Music by Lionel Bart

This piece needs a strong performance, but the middle section should be softer and smoother for contrast.

DANCE TO YOUR DADDY

English traditional

Accent the first beat of each bar slightly, but play the other notes quite lightly.

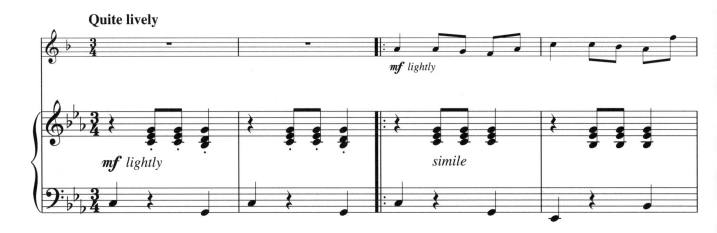

Pieces to Play

with

Step by Step

by

Edna Mae Burnam

To my grandson, David Bender

CONTENTS

A Canyon Deep 3

Stained Glass Window in a Church 4

The Shoemaker 5

Candles 7

Watching an Ice Skater 8

Sunset 10

A Garden 11

Holiday Time 12

ISBN 978-1-4234-3595-2

WILLIS MUSIC

EXCLUSIVELY DISTRIBUTED BY

HAL•LEONARD®

7777 W. BLUEMOUND RD. P.O. BOX 13819 MILWAUKEE, WI 53213

Visit Hal Leonard Online at
www.halleonard.com

TO THE TEACHER

The pieces in this book have been composed to correlate exactly with the Edna Mae Burnam Piano Course STEP BY STEP—Book Two. Prefixed to each piece is an indication of the exact page of STEP BY STEP—Book Two at which a selection from PIECES TO PLAY may be introduced. When the student reaches this page, he/she is ready to play with ease and understanding.

All of the pieces in this book may serve as repertoire for the student at this level.

The pieces in this book should be:

1. Perfected;
2. Memorized;
3. Played with expression and poise;
4. Kept in readiness to play for company.

Edna Mae Burnam

A CANYON DEEP

BY EDNA MAE BURNAM

Moderately fast, steady
medium loud

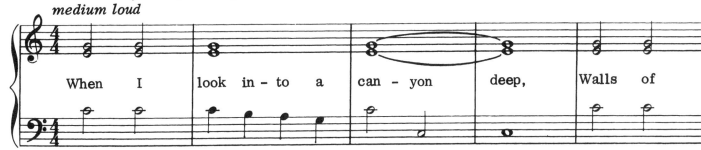

When I look in-to a can-yon deep, Walls of

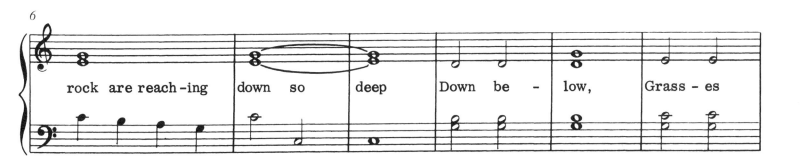

rock are reach-ing down so deep Down be - low, Grass-es

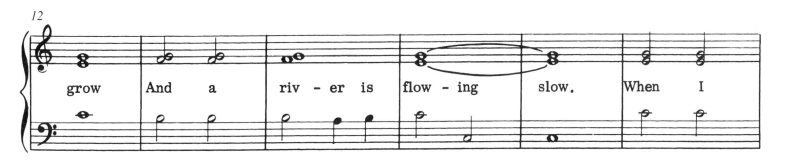

grow And a riv - er is flow - ing slow. When I

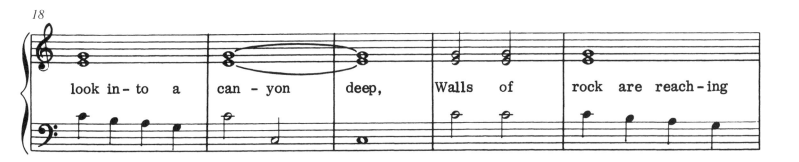

look in-to a can-yon deep, Walls of rock are reach-ing

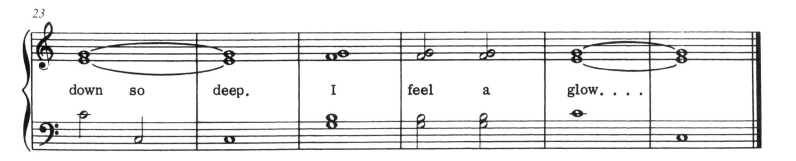

down so deep. I feel a glow. . . .

The student is ready to learn this piece after **page 16** of *Step by Step*, Book 2.

STAINED GLASS WINDOW IN A CHURCH

BY EDNA MAE BURNAM

Softly and sweetly

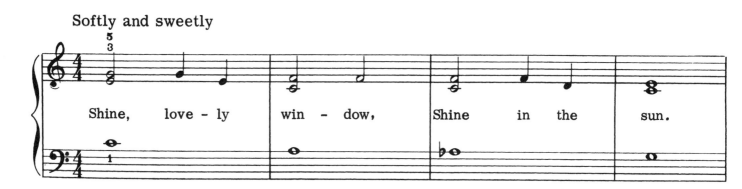

Shine, love - ly win - dow, Shine in the sun.

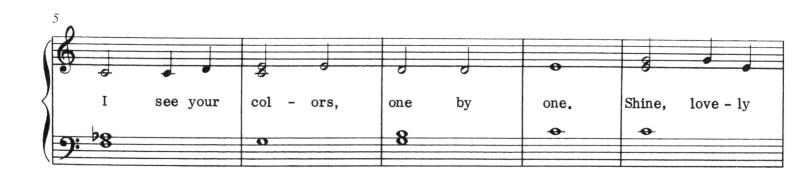

I see your col - ors, one by one. Shine, love - ly

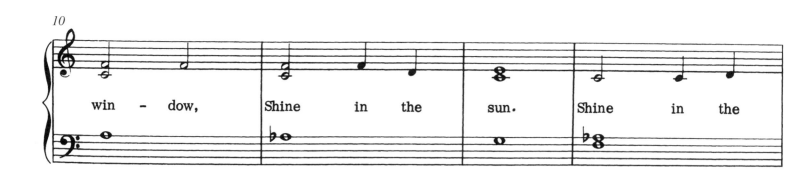

win - dow, Shine in the sun. Shine in the

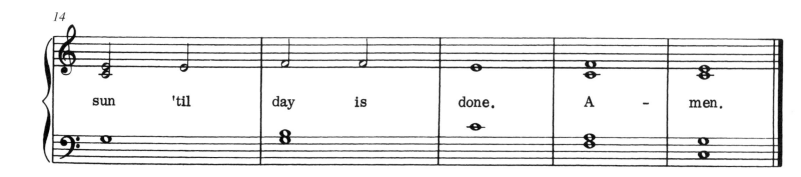

sun 'til day is done. A - men.

The student is ready to learn this piece after **page 19** of *Step by Step*, Book 2.

5

THE SHOEMAKER

BY EDNA MAE BURNAM

Moderately fast, busy and steady

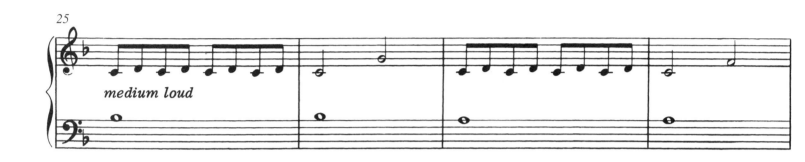

The student is ready to learn this piece after **page 25** of *Step by Step*, Book 2.

7

CANDLES

BY EDNA MAE BURNAM

Moderately fast
medium loud

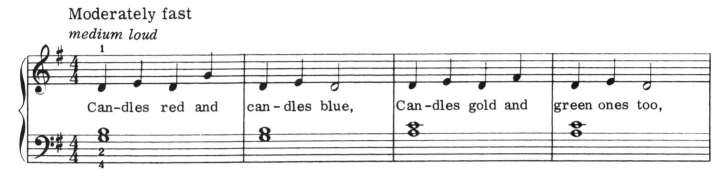

Can-dles red and can-dles blue, Can-dles gold and green ones too,

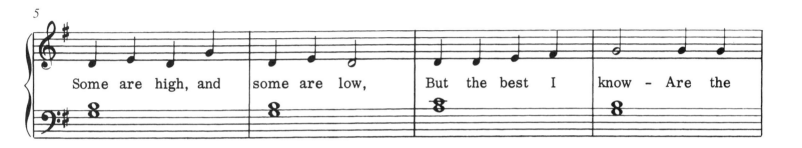

Some are high, and some are low, But the best I know - Are the

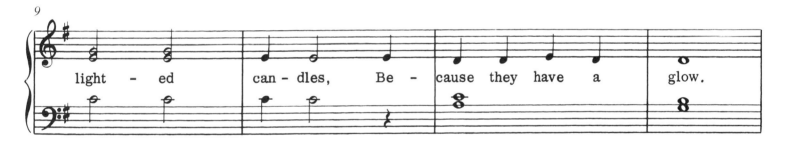

light - ed can - dles, Be - cause they have a glow.

Candle flame flickers as the candle is burning -

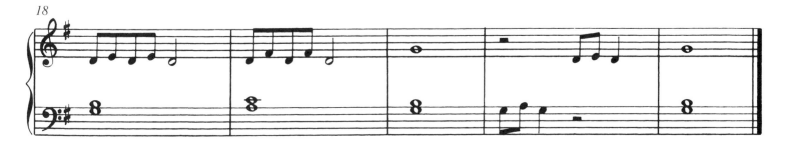

The student is ready to learn this piece after **page 30** of *Step by Step*, Book 2.

WATCHING AN ICE SKATER

BY EDNA MAE BURNAM

Moderately fast, like a waltz
light and free

The student is ready to learn this piece after **page 33** of *Step by Step*, Book 2.

SUNSET

BY EDNA MAE BURNAM

Languid, with a rocking motion in the left hand

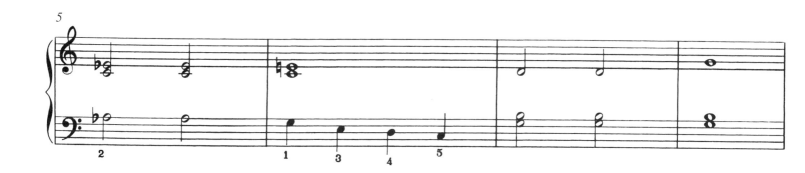

A GARDEN

BY EDNA MAE BURNAM

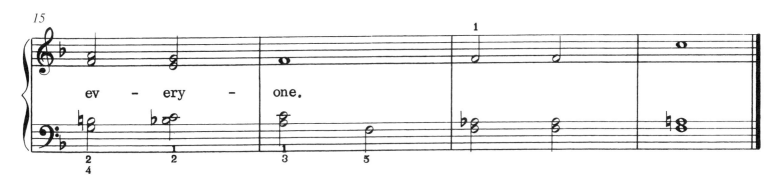

The student is ready to learn this piece after **page 41** of *Step by Step*, Book 2.

HOLIDAY TIME

BY EDNA MAE BURNAM

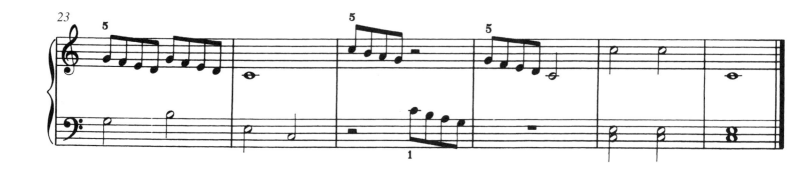

Certificate of Merit

This is to certify that

_____

has successfully completed

PIECES TO PLAY
BOOK TWO
BY
EDNA MAE BURNAM

and is now eligible for promotion to

PIECES TO PLAY
BOOK THREE

_____Teacher

Date _____

Edna Mae Burnam was a pioneer in piano publishing. The creator of the iconic *A Dozen a Day* technique series and *Step by Step* method was born on September 15, 1907 in Sacramento, California. She began lessons with her mother, a piano teacher who drove a horse and buggy daily through the Sutter Buttes mountain range to reach her students. In college Burnam decided that she too enjoyed teaching young children, and majored in elementary education at California State University (then Chico State College) with a minor in music. She spent several years teaching kindergarten in public schools before starting her own piano studio and raising daughters Pat and Peggy. She delighted in composing for her students, and took theory and harmony lessons from her husband David (a music professor and conductor of the Sacramento Symphony in the 1940s).

Burnam began submitting original pieces to publishers in the mid-1930s, and was thrilled when one of them, "The Clock That Stopped," was accepted, even though her remuneration was a mere $20. Undaunted, the industrious composer sent in the first *A Dozen a Day* manuscript to her Willis editor in 1950, complete with stick-figure sketches for each exercise. Her editor loved the simple genius of the playful artwork resembling a musical technique, and so did students and teachers: the book rapidly blossomed into a series of seven and continues to sell millions of copies. In 1959, the first book in the *Step by Step* series was published, with hundreds of individual songs and pieces along the way, often identified by whimsical titles in Burnam's trademark style.

The immense popularity of her books solidified Edna Mae Burnam's place and reputation in music publishing history, yet throughout her lifetime she remained humble and effervescent. "I always left our conversations feeling upbeat and happy," says Kevin Cranley, Willis president. "She could charm the legs off a piano bench," Bob Sylva of the *Sacramento Bee* wrote, "make a melody out of a soap bubble, and a song out of a moon beam."

Burnam died in 2007, a few months shy of her 100th birthday. "Music enriches anybody's life, even if you don't turn out to be musical," she said once in an interview. "I can't imagine being in a house without a piano."

A DOZEN A DAY

by Edna Mae Burnam

The **A Dozen A Day** books are universally recognized as one of the most remarkable technique series on the market for all ages! Each book in this series contains short warm-up exercises to be played at the beginning of each practice session, providing excellent day-to-day training for the student. All book/audio versions include orchestrated accompaniments by Ric Ianonne.

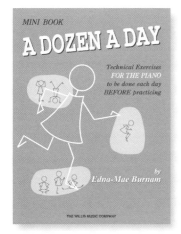

MINI BOOK
00404073 Book Only $5.99
00406472 Book/Audio $9.99

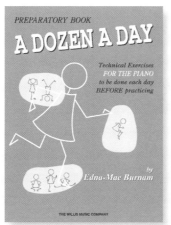

PREPARATORY BOOK
00414222 Book Only $5.99
00406476 Book/Audio $9.99

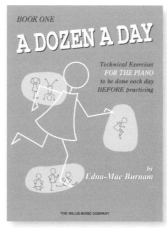

BOOK 1
00413366 Book Only $5.99
00406481 Book/Audio $9.99

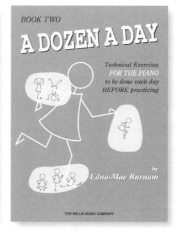

BOOK 2
00413826 Book Only $5.99
00406485 Book/Audio $9.99

BOOK 3
00414136 Book Only $6.99
00416760 Book/Audio $10.99

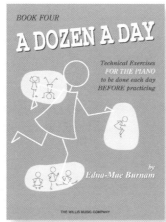

BOOK 4
00415686 Book Only $6.99
00416761 Book/Audio $10.99

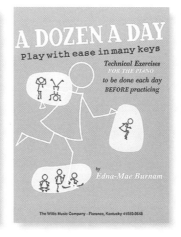

**PLAY WITH EASE
IN MANY KEYS**
00416395 Book Only $5.99

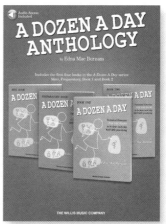

**A DOZEN A DAY
ANTHOLOGY**
00158307 Book/Audio $24.99

ALSO AVAILABLE:
The **A Dozen A Day Songbook** series containing Broadway, movie, and pop hits!

Visit Hal Leonard Online at **www.halleonard.com**

WILLIS MUSIC

EXCLUSIVELY DISTRIBUTED BY

HAL•LEONARD®

Prices, contents, and availability subject to change without notice.
Prices listed in U.S. funds.